THE
PEASANTS
ARE
REVOLTING

Brant Parker and Johnny Hart

A FAWCETT GOLD MEDAL BOOK

Fawcett Publications, Inc., Greenwich, Conn.

In the *WIZARD OF ID* Series:

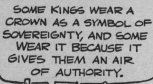

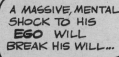

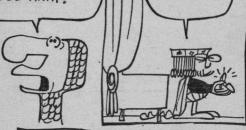

WHAT'S ALL THAT NOISE?

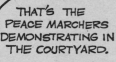

THAT'S THE PEACE MARCHERS DEMONSTRATING IN THE COURTYARD.

ARREST THEM!

FOR WHAT?

DISTURBING THE PEACE.

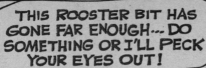

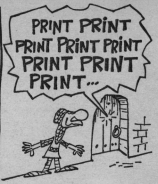

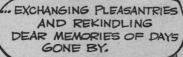